Hush!
and
Fib!

By **Clare Helen Welsh**

Illustrated by **Camilla Galindo**

The Letter U

Trace the lower and upper case letter with a finger. Sound out the letter.

Down,
around,
up,
down

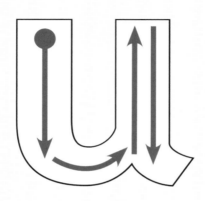

Down,
around,
up

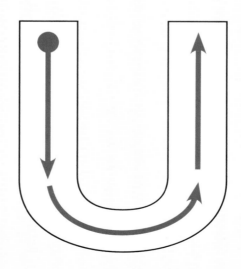

Some words to familiarise:

kids   bags   ducks

High-frequency words:

the a on at he is up in

Tips for Reading 'Hush!'

- Practise the words listed above before reading the story.

- If the reader struggles with any of the other words, ask them to look for sounds they know in the word. Encourage them to sound out the words and help them read the words if necessary.

- After reading the story, ask the reader why the kids say 'HUSH!' at the end of the story.

Fun Activity

Close your eyes and say what you can hear.

Hush!

Hum! Hum!

The kids sing a song.

Tap! Tap!
The kids bang the bags.

Chat! Chat!

The kids chat on the bus.

Ring! Ring!

The kids ring the bell.

Quack! Quack!
The kids quack at the ducks.

Puff! Puff!

The kids puff up the hill.

Huff! Huff!
The kids huff up the hill.

Kiss! Kiss!

Mum and Dad tuck the kids in.

Bash! Bam!

Bang! Thud!

Dash! Rush!

HUSH!

The Letter F

Trace the lower and upper case letter with a finger. Sound out the letter.

Around,
down,
lift,
cross

Down,
lift,
cross,
lift,
cross

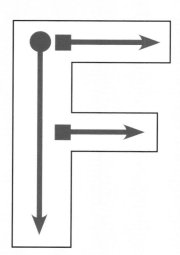

Some words to familiarise:

laptop   picnic   buns

High-frequency words:

on   the   it   no   is   a   up   his

Tips for Reading 'Fib!'

- Practise the words listed above before reading the story.

- If the reader struggles with any of the other words, ask them to look for sounds they know in the word. Encourage them to sound out the words and help them read the words if necessary.

- After reading the story, ask the reader why Chuck blames the ducks.

Fun Activity

Play a game of True or False!

Fib!

Chuck gets pen on the rug.

Chuck puts on the long top.
Rip!

23

Chuck sits on the laptop.

Chuck gets the picnic wet.

Mum and Dad cut up the buns.

Chuck licks his lips
and rubs his tum.

Yum!

Book Bands for Guided Reading

The Institute of Education book banding system is a scale of colours that reflects the various levels of reading difficulty. The bands are assigned by taking into account the content, the language style, the layout and phonics. Word, phrase and sentence level work is also taken into consideration.

Maverick Early Readers are a bright, attractive range of books covering the pink to white bands. All of these books have been book banded for guided reading to the industry standard and edited by a leading educational consultant.

To view the whole Maverick Readers scheme, visit our website at
www.maverickearlyreaders.com

Or scan the QR code above to view our scheme instantly!